What Is It?

Written by Linda Strachan

Illustrated by Mike Phillips

What a mess!

Dad got some wood.

Megan got some nails.

Dad nailed the wood together.

“Is it a boat?” asked David.

Dad put the roof on.

“Is it a dog house?”

asked David.

Megan got the rope

and Dad cut it.

"Is it a swing?" asked David.

KK331112

Megan got a rug.

She put it inside.

"What is it?" asked David.

"It's a tree house!"